CELEBRATION SERIES®

THE PIANO ODYSSEY®

PIANO
REPERTOIRE

6

ISBN 0-88797-695-6

FREDERICK
HARRIS
MUSIC

CELEBRATION SERIES®

THE PIANO ODYSSEY®

The *Celebration Series®* was originally published in 1987 to international acclaim. In 1994, a second edition was released and received with heightened enthusiasm. Launched in 2001 and building on the success of previous editions, the *Celebration Series®, The Piano Odyssey®* takes advantage of the wealth of new repertoire and the changing interests and needs of teachers.

The series is breathtaking in its scope, presenting a true musical odyssey through the ages and their respective musical styles. The albums are graded from late elementary to early intermediate (albums Introductory to 3) through intermediate (albums 4 to 8) to advanced and concert repertoire (albums 9 and 10). Each volume of repertoire comprises a carefully selected grouping of pieces from the Baroque, Classical, Romantic, and 20th-century style periods. *Studies/Etudes* albums present compositions especially suited for building technique as well as musicality relevant to the repertoire of each level. *Student Workbooks* and recordings are available to assist in the study and enjoyment of the music. In addition, the comprehensive *Handbook for Teachers* is an invaluable pedagogical resource.

A Note on Editing and Performance Practice

Most Baroque and early Classical composers wrote few dynamics, articulation, or other performance indications in their scores. Interpretation was left up to the performer, with the expectation that the performance practice was understood. In this edition, therefore, most of the dynamics and tempo indications in the Baroque and early Classical pieces have been added by the editors. These editorial markings, including fingering and the execution of ornaments, are intended to be helpful rather than definitive.

The keyboard instruments of the 17th and early 18th centuries lacked the sustaining power of the modern piano. Consequently, the usual keyboard touch was detached rather than legato. The pianist should assume that a lightly detached touch is appropriate for Baroque and early Classical music, unless a different approach is indicated by the style of the music.

Even into the 19th century, composers' scores could vary from copy to copy or edition to edition. Thus, the editors of the *Celebration Series®* have also made editorial choices in much of the Classical and Romantic repertoire presented in the series.

This edition follows the policy that the bar line cancels accidentals. In accordance with current practice, cautionary accidentals are added only in cases of possible ambiguity.

Teachers and students should refer to the companion guides – the *Student Workbooks* and the *Handbook for Teachers* – for further discussion of style and pedagogical elements. For examination requirements of The Royal Conservatory of Music, please refer to the current *Piano Syllabus*.

Dr. Trish Sauerbrei
Editor-in-Chief

Contents

Little Prelude in D Minor
BWV 926

Johann Sebastian Bach
(1685 – 1750)

The slurs in mm. 9 – 10 and 13 – 14 are original.
Most quarter notes should be played detached.

Source: *Neun kleine Präludien (BWV 924-932)* from *Clavierbüchlein vor Wilhelm Friedemann Bach* (1720)

0-88797-695-6 / 04

Allemande in A Minor

HWV 478

George Frideric Handel
(1685 – 1759)

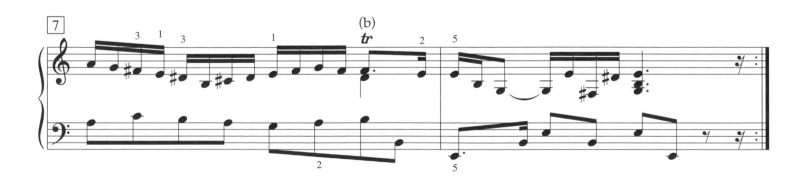

Left-hand eighth notes may be played slightly detached.

Minuet in G Minor

Gottfried Heinrich Stölzel
(1690 – 1749)

Source: *Partia di Signore Steltzeln* from *Clavierbüchlein vor Wilhelm Friedemann Bach* (1720)

0-88797-695-6 / 08

Sarabanda in G Minor

Domenico Zipoli
(1688 – 1726)

Source: Suite in G Minor from *Sonate d'Intavolatura per Organo e Cimbalo*, op. 1 (1716)

0-88797-695-6 / 09

Bourrée in A Minor

Johann Ludwig Krebs
(1713 – 1780)

Source: Partita in A Minor

0-88797-695-6 / 10

Sonata in A Major
LS 31, K 83
II: Minuetto

Domenico Scarlatti
(1685 – 1757)

Divertimento in G Major
Hob. XVI:G1

I

Franz Joseph Haydn
(1732 – 1809)

Allegro ♩ = 88 – 100

(a) The stroke (ᵛ) indicates *staccato*.

Sonatina in G Major

op. 20, no. 1

I

Jan Ladislav Dussek
(1760 – 1812)

Allegro non tanto ♩ = 112 – 120

Sonatina in F Major
op. 36, no. 4

I

Muzio Clementi
(1752 – 1832)

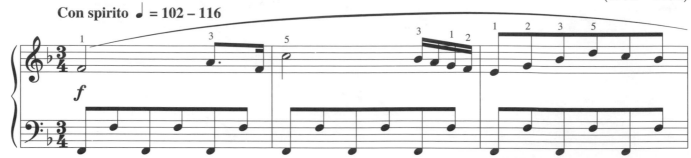

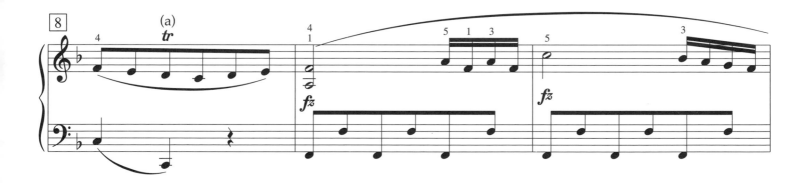

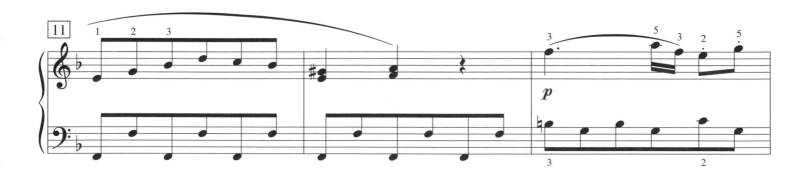

(a)

For examinations, play any one movement.

Source: *Six Progressive Sonatinas for the Piano Forte,* op. 36 (1797)

0-88797-695-6 / 18

20

II

Andante con espressione ♩ = 48 – 58

For examinations, play any one movement.

III: Rondo

For examinations, play any one movement.

Bagatelle

op. 119, no. 9

Ludwig van Beethoven
(1770 – 1824)

Source: *Elf Bagatellen*, op. 119 (1820 – 1822)

0-88797-695-6 / 27

Sonatina in F Major
op. 168, no. 1
III: Rondo

Anton Diabelli
(1781 – 1858)

Allegretto ♩. = 88 – 96

Source: *Musikalische Morgenstunden, 1. Woche. 7 Sonatinen*, op. 168

Sentimental Waltz

op. 50, no. 13

Franz Schubert
(1797 – 1828)

Source: *Valses sentimentales*, op. 50, D 797 (Vienna, 1825)

Waltz in A Minor
op. 124, no. 4

Robert Schumann
(1810 – 1856)

Lebhaft* ♩. = 52 – 63

con pedale

Composed 1835

* Lively

Source: *Albumblätter,* op. 124 (Elberfeld, 1854)

Arietta

op. 12, no. 1

Edvard Grieg
(1843 – 1907)

Source: *Lyric Pieces*, op. 12 (Copenhagen, 1867)

Miniature Waltz
op. 10, no. 10

Vladimir Ivanovich Rebikov
(1866 – 1920)

Source: *Stimmungsskizzen*, op. 10

0-88797-695-6 / 33

Warrior's Dance

op. 27, no. 19

Dmitri Kabalevsky
(1904 – 1987)

Source: *Children's Pieces,* op. 27 (1937 – 1938)
Permission to reprint granted by G. Schirmer, Inc. (ASCAP); Boosey & Hawkes, Inc.; Internationale Musikverlage
Hans Sikorski; Le Chant du Monde; and Zenon Music Company Ltd. for their respective territories.

Pastoral Dance

op. 24, no. 4

Paul Creston
(1906 – 1985)

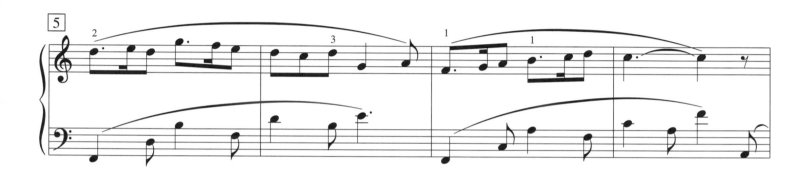

Source: *Five Little Dances*, op. 24

Bright Orange

Robert Starer
(1924 –)

Source: *Sketches in Color: Seven Pieces for Piano*
© 1964 (Renewed) Universal-MCA Music Publishing, a Division of Universal Studios, Inc. All rights reserved.
Reprinted by permission of Warner Bros. Publications U.S. Inc., Miami, FL 33014.

An Ancient Tale

Bohdana Filtz
(1932 –   )

Source: *Souvenirs for Piano: Town and Country*

0-88797-695-6 / 40

March of the Buffoons

Dale Reubart
(1926 –   )

Source: *Pantomimes*

For Susanna Kyle

born July 24, 1949

Leonard Bernstein
(1918 – 1990)

Sarabande

Pierre Gallant
(1950 –   )

Roundup

André Previn
(1929 –   )

Source: *Impressions for Piano: Twenty Pieces for Students*

Miniature

Miroslav Lebeda
(1922 –   )

Source: *Souvenirs for Piano: Piano Sketches*
© Copyright 1995 The Frederick Harris Music Co., Limited, Mississauga, Ontario, Canada.

0-88797-695-6 / 47

Cancan

Douglas Finch
(1957 –   )

0-88797-695-6 / 48